# Chart Topping DRUM FILLS

## By Dawn Richardson

# The 60s through Today

**Get the accompanying video course by Dawn Richardson**

onlinedrummer.com/chart-topping-drum-fills/

OnlineDrummer.com
PO Box 351
Madison, OH 44057

# About the Author

Dawn Richardson is a San Francisco based drummer and teacher. She believes anyone can play the drums and encourages all who are interested to try it out! Dawn has taught students ranging in age from three to sixty three with an equally wide range of drumming aspirations. Dawn strives to help each individual reach his or her musical goals using proven teaching materials and methods to help promote proper technique, while continuing to be open to creating new approaches to helping students learn. That perspective has manifested into various method books and videos to date.

Dawn's book, "Building Blocks of Rock, Fundamental Patterns and Exercises for the Rock Drummer" (1998) has been well received by students and teachers alike as a beginning drum method. Other titles that are available through Mel Bay Publications include the following method books and charts: "Kid's Rock Drum Method" (2011); "Beginning Rock Drum Chart" (2009); "Block Rockin' Beats" (2006); "Fill Workbook, Short Fills and the Tools to Create Your Own" (2005).

Dawn has also toured or recorded with a wide range of diverse musical artists such as Tracy Chapman, Joey Santiago (The Pixies), Joe Gore (P.J. Harvey/DJ Shadow), Vicki Randle (The Tonight Show), Shana Morrison, Penelope Houston and The Loud Family, to name a few. Dawn is perhaps best known for her work as the drummer of 4 Non Blondes. As a member of that successful rock band, she received gold and platinum records for sales in the United States along with thirteen gold records and nine platinum singles for international sales. She toured the world, opening for such rock legends as Aerosmith, Neil Young, Pearl Jam, and Prince and has appeared on national and international television performing live on Late Night with David Letterman, The Late Show with Conan O'Brien, MTV's Beach House, The Billboard Music Awards, and England's Top of the Pops.

Dawn got her start on drum kit with Jim Volpe and Jim Vessiny in Southern California. She holds her Bachelor of Arts Degree in Percussion from Cal State Los Angeles and has studied with the principal percussionist of the Los Angeles Philharmonic, Raynor Carroll and with studio greats Steve Houghton and Greg Goodall. Dawn is endorsed by Zildjian Cymbals, Vic Firth Sticks, Drum Workshop Hardware and Pedals, and Pacific Drums.

e-mail: books@onlinedrummer.com
website: www.dawnrichardson.com
YouTube Channel: dawnrichardsonsf

# Table of Contents

# Lesson 1

# Build Fills

# INTRO TO BUILD-FILLS

A ***build-fill*** is a basic, yet powerful, drum fill which builds into the next section usually with a ***crescendo*** or by gradually getting louder. You will see the symbol for *crescendo* throughout this lesson.

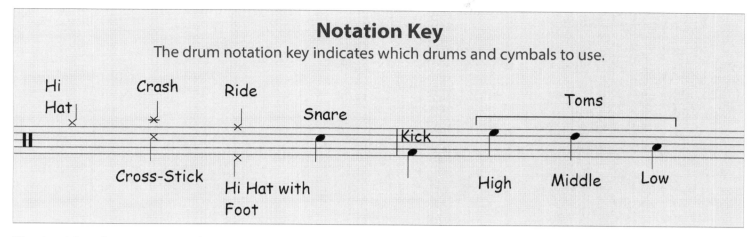

## Notation Key
The drum notation key indicates which drums and cymbals to use.

The build technique is used in the hit song *Highway to Hell* by AC/DC (1979). Play the main beat below 3 times, play the fill into the chorus, and then play the chorus main beat.

## Highway to Hell
*AC/DC 1979*

The build-fill is used in "Highway to Hell" to lead into the chorus.

♩ = 117

# CHART-TOPPERS

Many chart-topping songs use the build-fill technique. Try these fills from hit songs.

### Sweet Child O' Mine
*Guns N' Roses 1988*

Here are 3 of the build-fills from this classic rock song.

♩ = 128

**Intro Build**

**Fill into Lead Break 2**

**Bridge to Outro**

### Buddy Holly
*Weezer 1994*

♩ = 121

**Pre-chorus**

**Build into Chorus**

6    Chart-Topping Drum Fills – *The 60s Through Today*

# CHART-TOPPERS (cont.)

### Heart Shaped Box
*Nirvana (1993)*

This song uses a number of build-fills to transition to the chorus.

♩ = 100

Verse Main Beat

Transition to Chorus

Start of Chorus

(etc.)

End of Chorus

# CHART-TOPPERS (cont.)

## Come Out and Play

*The Offspring 1994*

$\quad = 160$

**Main Beat**

**Build into Chorus**

## Midnight Special

*Creedence Clearwater Revival 1969*

In the following fills, note how many variations there are on one idea.

$\quad = 124$

**Fills to Chorus**

"

"

"

Chart-Topping Drum Fills – *The 60s Through Today*

# COORDINATION BUILDING

The following one-bar fills will work well at most tempos. Practice them with one or three bars of time. The first example below can be used as a template. Most of the build-fills work well with multiple kick drum variations as well. Examples for the kick drum variations that might be appropriate for these fills are shown in the lettered variations below. The variation you choose will depend on many factors including song context, tempo and style.

## ONE-MEASURE BUILD-FILLS

### Kick Technique Examples

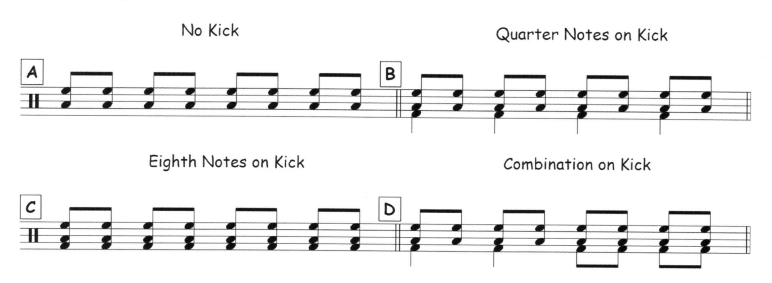

### Practice Template

# COORDINATION BUILDING (cont.)

Try these coordination building exercises below. Remember you can practice them with one or three bars of time, like shown in the practice template on page 9. This section is written for 2 toms. If you have 3 toms, experiment with substituting the middle tom for the high and/or low.

| ONE-MEASURE BUILD-FILLS (cont.) |
|---|

## Exercises

(half-open/sloshy hi-hat)

# COORDINATION BUILDING (cont.)

Here are more exercises for you to try. These exercises develop your skills at playing partial measure build-fills. Remember you can use the second line below as a two-measure template for practicing the fills. You can also substitute any beat you like for practice. The slashes below indicate time and are used so that you can better see the placement of the fill.

**PARTIAL-MEASURE BUILD-FILLS**

### Practice Template

Drum Fill

### Exercises

# COORDINATION BUILDING (cont.)

The following fills are longer build-fills and work well at most tempos. Once again, feel free to substitute any beat you like for practice.

## LONG BUILD-FILLS

**Exercises**

*Chart-Topping Drum Fills – The 60s Through Today*

# COMPOSITION

These templates will help you get started creating your own build-fills. After you are familiar with the song examples and coordination building sections of this lesson, try to create some of your own fills and beats below. The second two measures in the last two templates are open so that you can write another bar of time or make a longer fill.

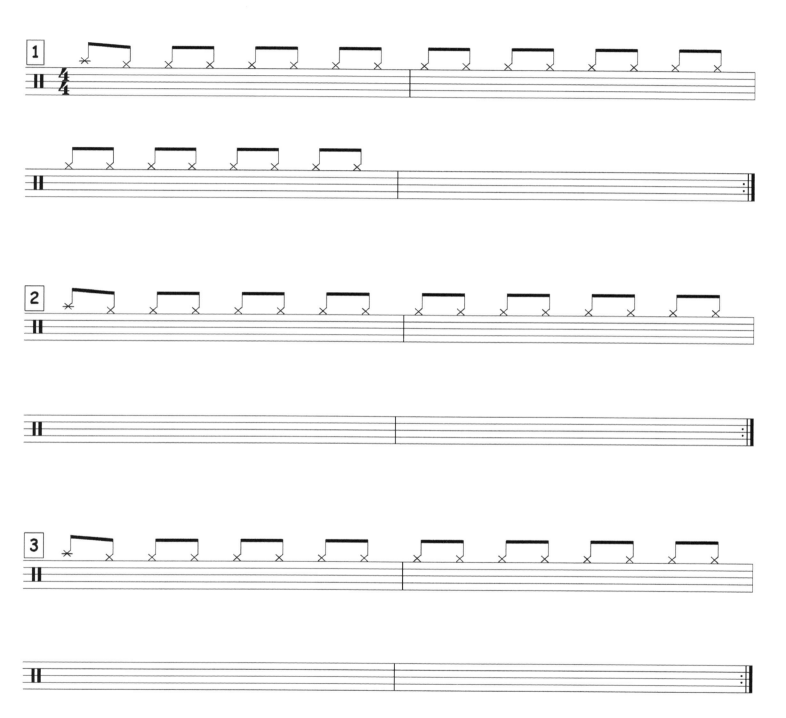

# Lesson 2

# Short Fills

# INTRO TO SHORT FILLS

Short fills are everywhere! Here are a few song examples so that you can hear them in context. Once you learn these, you will no doubt be able to hear them in songs more easily. Enjoy learning some of these variations, and then try to create some of your own. Remember that the fill needs to "fit" with the rest of the song. Often, shorter is better, so it's great to practice and learn many variations of these short fills.

### Rollin' in the Deep

*Adele 2010*

The ○ above the hi-hat stroke means to open the hi-hat and + means to close it.

# CHART-TOPPERS

Here are some examples of short fills for you to explore.

### Swallowed
*Bush 1996*

♩ = 90

**Chorus Fill 1**

**Chorus Fill 2**

### Time Bomb
*Rancid 1995*

♩ = 165

**Chorus (in & out)**

# CHART-TOPPERS (cont.)

There are a lot of short fills in the song *Honey Bee* by Blake Shelton (2011).

### Honey Bee
*Blake Shelton 2011*

♩ = 104 *(w/light swing)*

# CHART-TOPPERS (cont.)

Check out the short-fills used in *Play That Funky Music* by Wild Cherry (1976).

### Play That Funky Music
*Wild Cherry 1976*

♩ = 109

**Intro Pick-up Fill**

**Fill Into Verse 1**

L R L R L R L R

**Chorus Fill**

L R L

**Verse to Pre-Chorus**

R L R L R L

**Pre-Chorus to 2nd Chorus**

R L R L R L R

# COORDINATION BUILDING

The following short fills will work well at most tempos. Practice these in two or four-measure phrases. The first example is written out as a two-bar phrase and can be used as a template.

You might choose to help keep time through the two-beat fills by playing quarter notes or eighth notes with the bass drum, depending on the tempo and type of song or context. In general, it's probably easier and more helpful to do more with the kick if you are playing at slower tempos. It might get too busy playing the kick during short fills at faster tempos. Again, these exercises are written for a kit with two toms. You can substitute your extra toms if your kit has more.

## Exercises

# COORDINATION BUILDING (cont.)

**Exercises (cont.)**

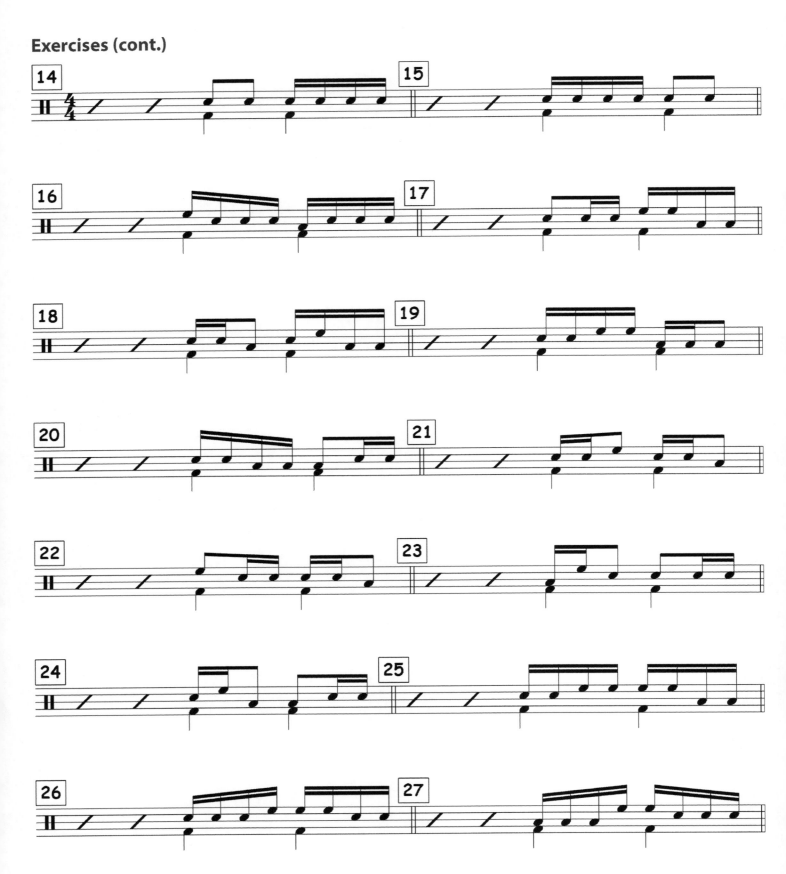

# COMPOSITION

These templates will help you get started creating your own short fills. After you are familiar with the song examples and coordination building sections of this lesson, try to create some of your own fills and write them here. The first two templates are for one beat or shorter fills. The rest of the worksheet can be used for two beat fills. Have fun and be creative!

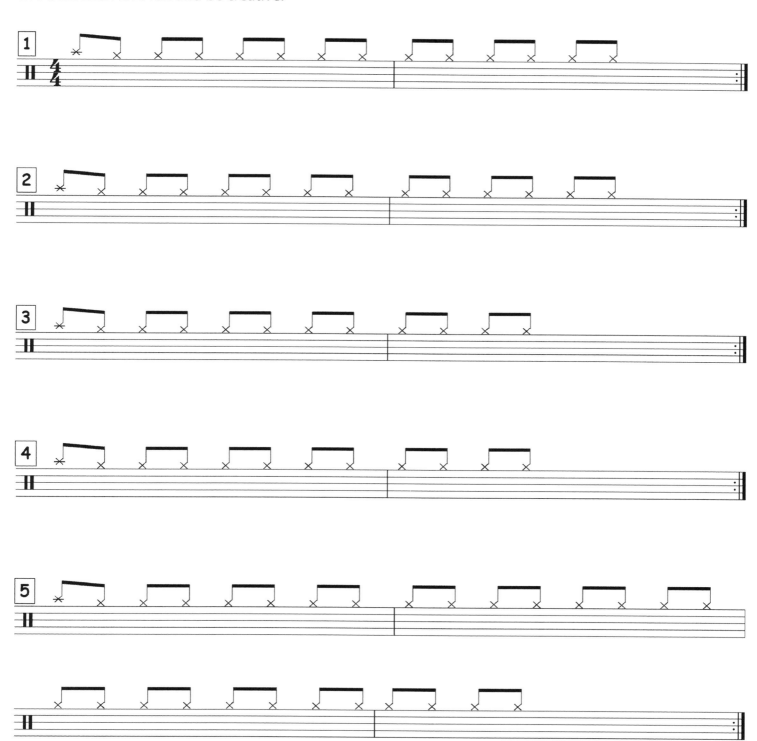

# Lesson 3

# Sixteenth-note Fills

# INTRO TO SIXTEENTH-NOTE FILLS

Sixteenth notes are the quintessential fill note value. You hear these types of fills often and in varied musical genres. You will no doubt find plenty more songs using this concept than are included here. Check out the various songs with these fills, and then try making up your own. Always keep in mind that the fills should compliment the rest of the music. Try to keep your fills appropriate for the situation.

### Come As You Are
*Nirvana 1992*

# CHART-TOPPERS

Try the following chart-topping fills using sixteenth notes from *All Right Now* by Free (1970).

**All Right Now**

*Free (1970)*

♩ = 120

Fill Into
Chorus
1 & 2

Break-
down

(closed roll)

Fill out
of Solo

Fill Into
Last
Chorus

Fills in
Last
Chorus

"

Chart-Topping Drum Fills – *The 60s Through Today*

# CHART-TOPPERS (cont.)

Here are more chart-topping examples of sixteenths in drum fills.

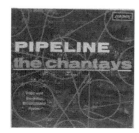

### Pipeline
*The Chantays (1962)*

♩ = 160

**Intro/A Section Fills**

**"**

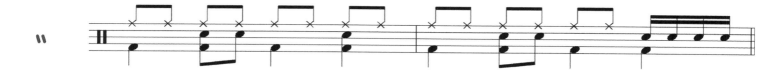

**"**

**Walk-down to Break**

# CHART-TOPPERS (cont.)

### Breed

*Nirvana (1991)*

♩ = 160

Big
Intro
Fill

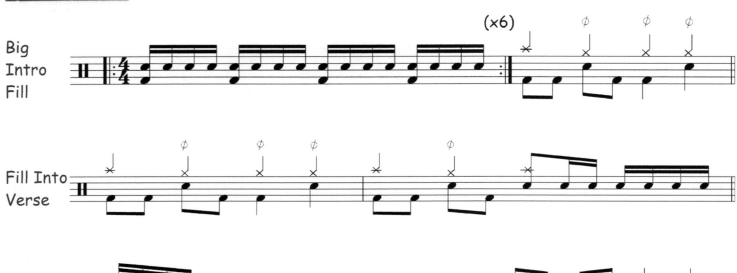

Fill Into
Verse

Fill Into
Chorus

### Play That Funky Music

*Wild Cherry 1976*

♩ = 109

Fill Into
Chorus

# COORDINATION BUILDING

Here are some more ideas for one-measure sixteenth note fills. These are written for three toms and include some favorites that you will most likely recognize. The first example is written out and can be used as a four bar template for all of the fills. You can substitute any beat you like for practice. Hopefully this will get you moving your fills around the kit and also give you some more ideas for new fill concepts.

## Practice Template

Drum Fill

## Exercises

# COORDINATION BUILDING (cont.)

## Exercises (cont.)

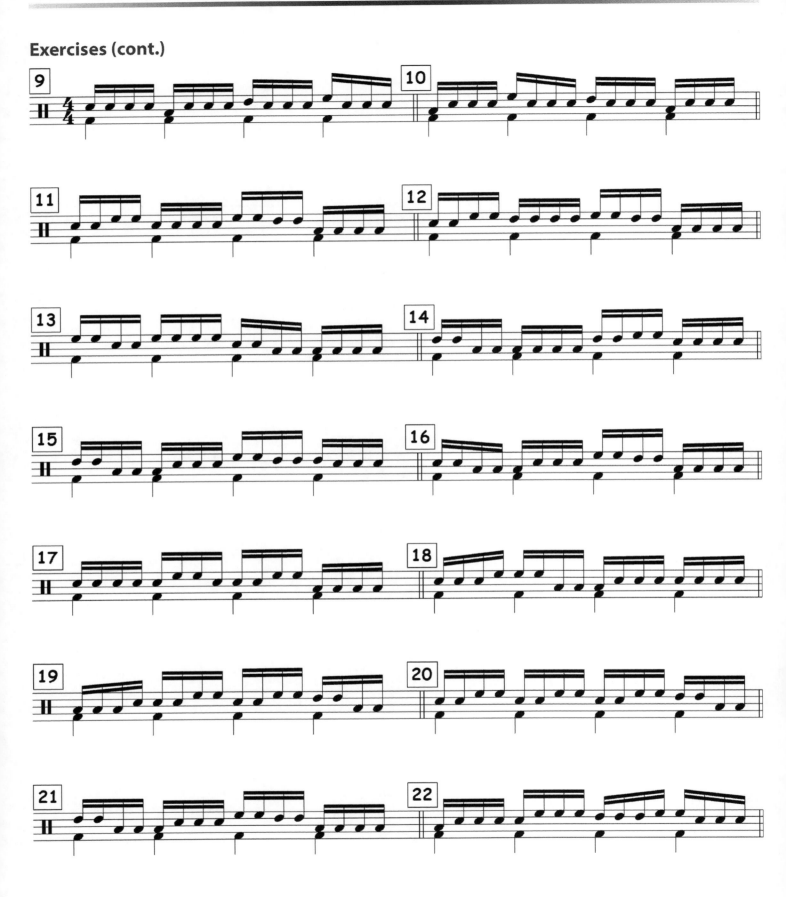

# COORDINATION BUILDING (cont.)

**Exercises (cont.)**

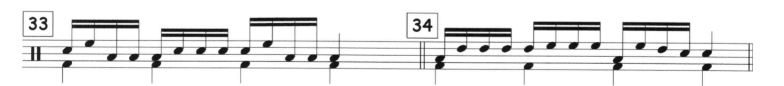

# COORDINATION BUILDING (cont.)

**Exercises (cont.)**

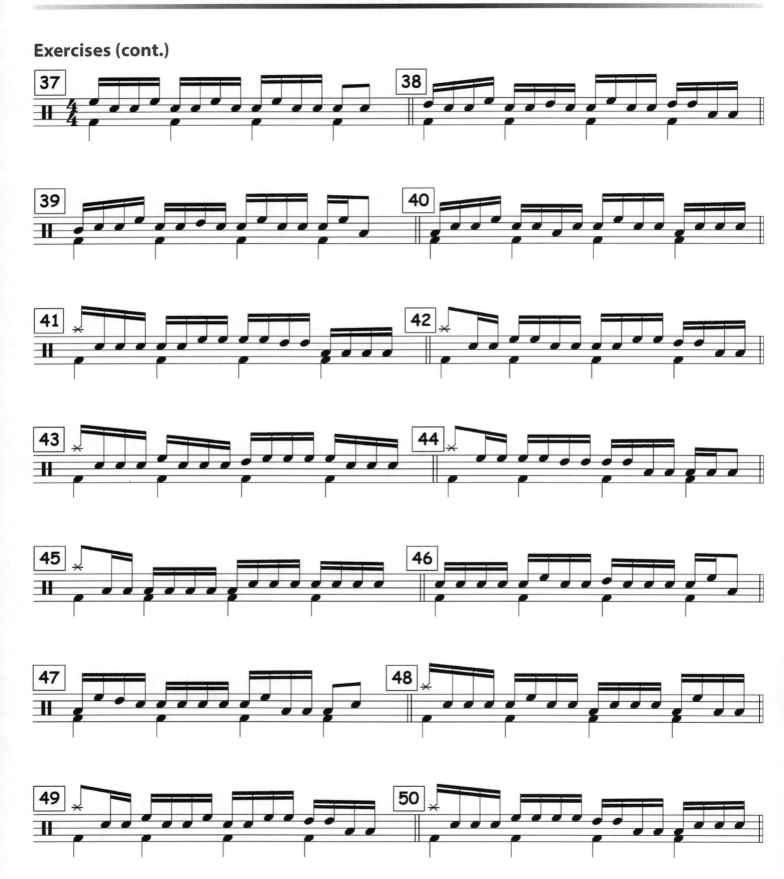

# COMPOSITION

These templates will help you get started creating your own sixteenth note fills. After you are familiar with the song examples and coordination building sections of this lesson, try to create some of your own fills and write them. Although these fills could be virtually any length, these templates are created so that you can write them as one measure or shorter.

# Lesson 4

# Around the Toms

# INTRO TO FILLS AROUND THE TOMS

These are the fills we all couldn't wait to play when we first started drumming! The following songs all have great examples of fills going around the toms. At this point though, we are encountering a lot of overlap with the fill techniques. Many of these fills incorporate techniques from previous lessons, which will be good practice.

### Because the Night

*Bruce Springsteen & The E Street Band (1969)*

♩ = 116

**Fill Into First Chorus**

**Fill Into Second Chorus**

**Bridge Fill 1**

**Bridge Fill 2**

# CHART-TOPPERS

The following examples are from *Whole Lotta Love* by Led Zeppelin (1969)

## Whole Lotta Love

*Led Zeppelin (1969)*

Chart-Topping Drum Fills – *The 60s Through Today*

# CHART-TOPPERS (cont.)

The following fills are continued from the previous page.

### Whole Lotta Love (cont.)
*Led Zeppelin (1969)*

♩ = 80

(After the second breakdown, when the drums re-enter)

Last Chorus & Outro

"

"

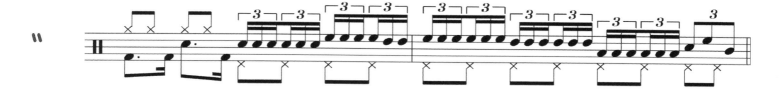

### Brick House
*The Commodores (1977)*

♩ = 106

Intro Fill

After Break-down

# CHART-TOPPERS (cont.)

### Rock Steady
*Aretha Franklin (1972)*

♩ = 104

A note with parentheses around it indicates a **ghost stroke**. In other words, hit that note very lightly.

**Into B Section**

### White Room
*Cream (1968)*

♩ = 116

**Verse Fill**

### Barracuda
*Heart (1977)*

♩ = 132

**Outro Fill**

# CHART-TOPPERS (cont.)

### I Want to Hold Your Hand

*The Beatles (1963)*

$\quad \bullet = 136$

**Chorus Fill**

**Outro – Chorus Fill**

# COORDINATION BUILDING

Here are some more fills around the toms. These are writen for three toms and the template uses the same fill as Lesson 3 to get you started. Feel free to substitute any beat you like for practice and mix things up to keep it interesting.

## Practice Template

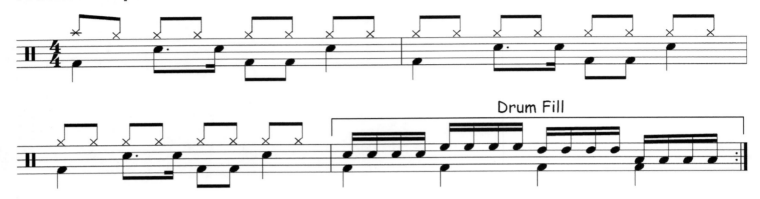

## Exercises

# COORDINATION BUILDING (cont.)

**Exercises (cont.)**

# COORDINATION BUILDING (cont.)

## Exercises (cont.)

*Chart-Topping Drum Fills – The 60s Through Today*

# COMPOSITION

These templates will help you get started creating your own fills going around the toms. After you are familiar with the song examples and coordination building sections of this lesson, try to create some of your own fills, and write them. These fills could be any length, but these templates are created so that you can write them as one measure or shorter. Try to mix up the rhythmic figures to create new and interesting fills.

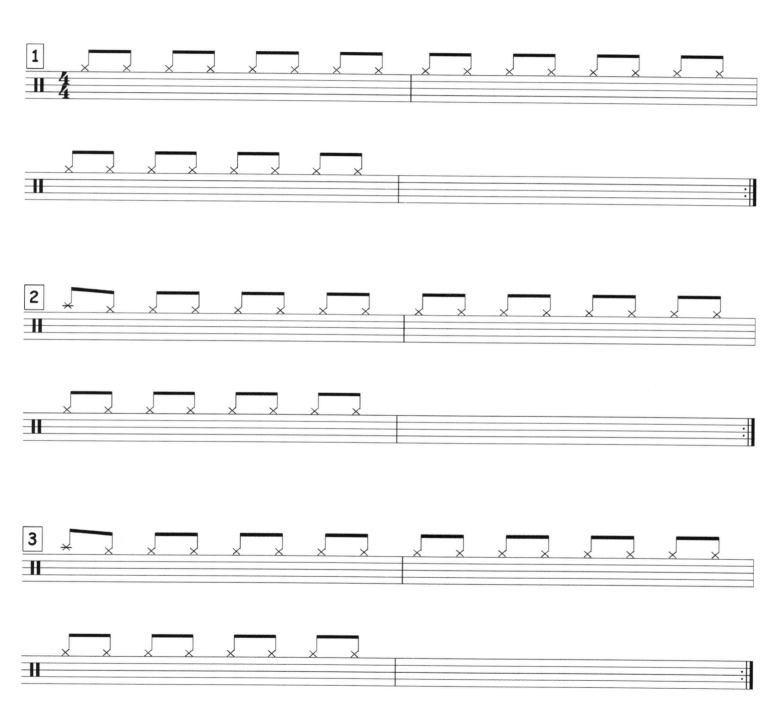

# Lesson 5

# Crashes in your Fills

# INTRO TO CRASHES IN YOUR FILLS

Sometimes a crash (or two) is the perfect choice as a fill for a song. These examples illustrate that point quite well. Some of the song examples below have crashes as fills and others have great examples of combining crashes with other elements. Try to create some crash fills of your own after completing the following chapter, and experiment with placement in songs.

**Beverly Hills**

*Weezer (2005)*

# CHART-TOPPERS

## Rockin' in the Free World
*Neil Young (1989)*

♩ = 132

**Chorus Main Beat**

**Transit-ion To Solo**

**Fill Into Final Verse**

## Barracuda
*Heart (1977)*

♩ = 132

**Intro & Verse Fill**

**Fill Into Bridge**

**Outro Fill**

Chart-Topping Drum Fills – *The 60s Through Today*

# CHART-TOPPERS (cont.)

### Back in Black
*AC/DC (1980)*

Intro
To
Verse 1

End of
Chorus

Solo
Phrases

Fill Into
Bridge

### Walk
*Foo Fighters (2011)*

Chorus
Fill

# COORDINATION BUILDING

Here are some more fills with crashes in them and ideas for crashes as fills. In this section, we will begin with shorter examples, and then give some various fill lengths as the lesson progresses. These examples are written for snare, but also try orchestrating rhythms around the kit by substituting the snare with toms.

## Practice Template

## Exercises

Chart-Topping Drum Fills – *The 60s Through Today*

# COORDINATION BUILDING (cont.)

## Exercises (cont.)

# COORDINATION BUILDING (cont.)

**Exercises (cont.)**

**TWO-BAR PATTERNS**

Chart-Topping Drum Fills – *The 60s Through Today*

# COMPOSITION

These templates will help you get started creating your own fills with crashes. After you are familiar with the song examples and coordination building sections of this lesson, try to create some of your own fills, and write them. The templates in this lesson are of varied lengths so that you can work on fills at various lengths.

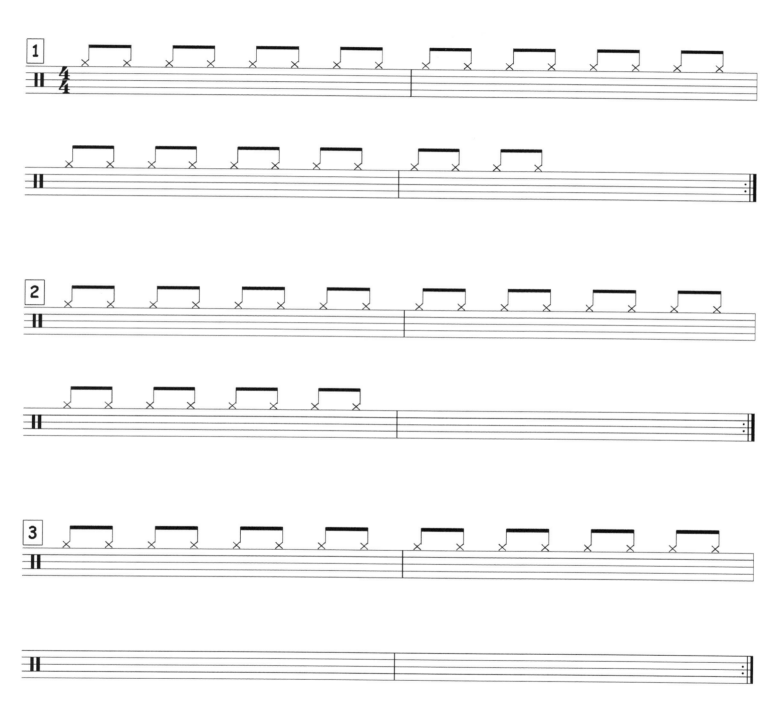

# Lesson 6

# Syncopated Fills

# INTRO TO SYNCOPATED FILLS

This lesson focuses on syncopated drum fills. After practicing these fills from the context of the song examples, try creating your own syncopated fills. Depending on the rest of the music and parts, keep your fills appropriate for the musical situation. The example songs will give you a good basis to get started with these types of fills.

### Shotgun

*Junior Walker and the All Stars (1965)*

♩ = 120        (Also at the end of most verses and chorus)

Intro Fill

### D'yer Mak'er

*Led Zeppelin (1973)*

♩ = 77

Verse 1 Fill

Fill Into First Chorus

Fill Into Solo

Outro Fill

# CHART-TOPPERS

The following examples from chart-topping songs use syncopated drum fills. Give them a try!

### Crosstown Traffic
*Jimi Hendrix (1968)*

♩ = 112

**Intro Fill**

(Also in Chorus 3 & 4)

**End of First Verse**

**End of Second Verse**

**Outro Fill**

# CHART-TOPPERS (cont.)

## Born to be Wild
*Steppenwolf (1968)*

♩ = 146

**End of Solo**

## Hang Loose
*Alabama Shakes (2012)*

♩ = 120

**Chorus Fill**

**Fill Into Second Verse**

# COORDINATION BUILDING

Here are some exercises to help create your own syncopated fills. The first example is a template and can be used for all of the fills. Substitute any beat you like for practice. As always, feel free to re-orchestrate the fills onto different drums when you are comfortable with the rhythms.

## Practice Template

## Exercises

# COORDINATION BUILDING (cont.)

**Exercises (cont.)**

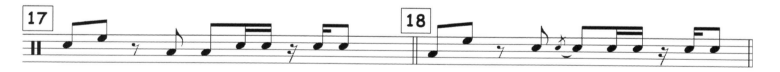

# COORDINATION BUILDING (cont.)

## TWO-BAR PATTERNS

**Practice Template**

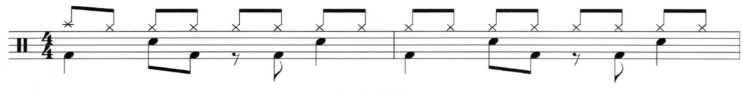

Drum Fill

**Exercises**

1

2

3

4

# COMPOSITION

These templates will help you get started creating syncopated fills. After you are familiar with the song examples and coordination building sections of this lesson, try to create some of your own fills using syncopation, and write them. The templates in this lesson are one or two bars, as that was what we saw in the song examples in this lesson. You can also try to make shorter fills, if you would like.

# Lesson 7

## Developing Your Style

# DEVELOPING YOUR STYLE

If you've made it this far, you've learned many drum fill techniques and combinations used in chart-topping songs from the 60s through today.  Now it's time to apply those techniques and combinations in your own way to develop your own style. Improvising fills can be difficult, but stay relaxed and focus on playing fills that match the feel of the overall piece.

This last lesson leaves you with practice templates to use while applying the drum fill vocabulary you've learned. Where the slashes indicate, play time, or in other words, play a drum beat of your choice. Play drum fills on the beats indicated. Try to keep it interesting, playing different fills each time. Be creative!

## Template #1

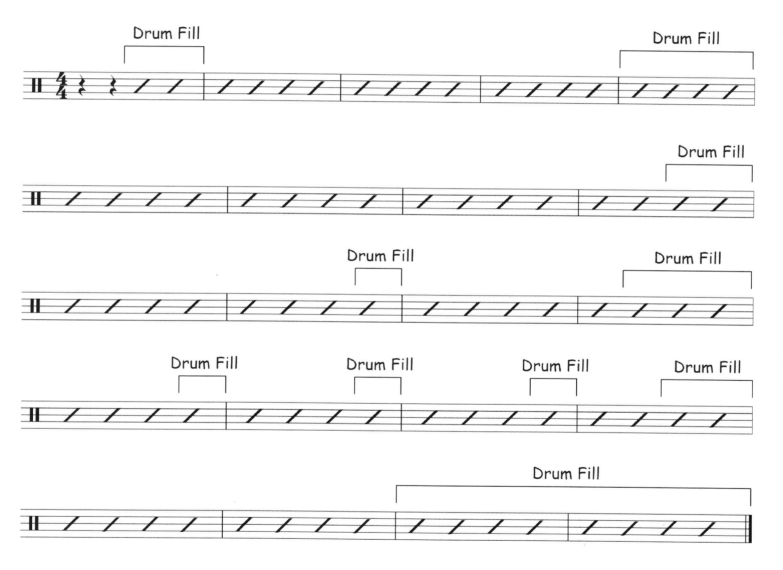

# DEVELOPING YOUR STYLE (CONT.)

**Template #2**

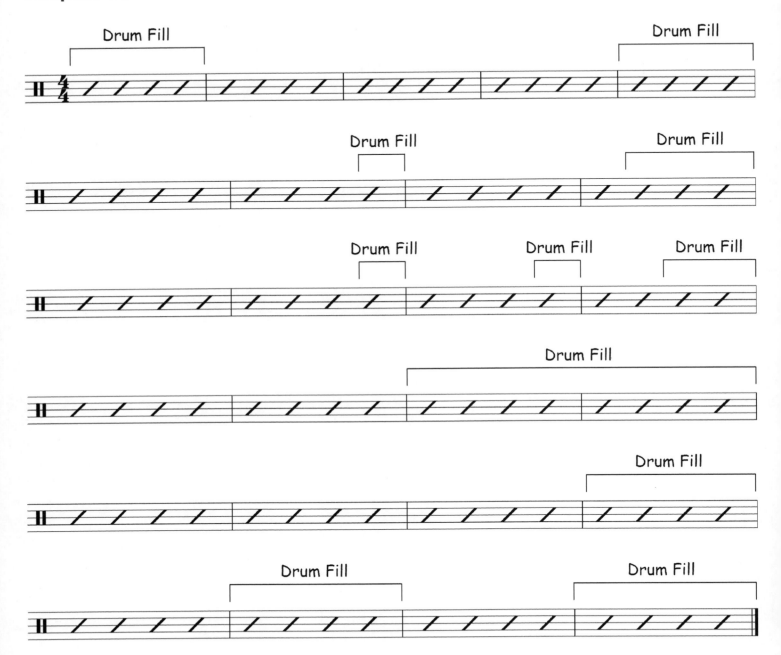

# DEVELOPING YOUR STYLE (CONT.)

**Template #3**

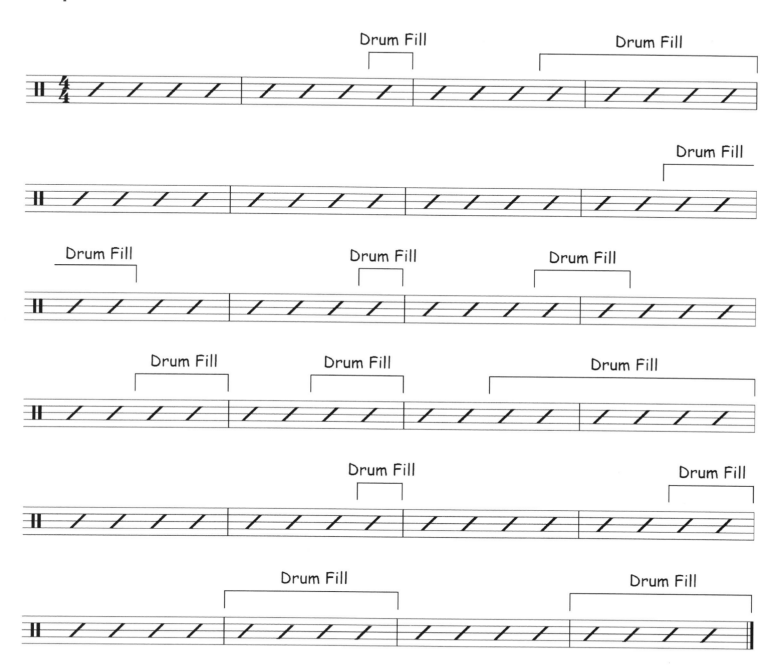

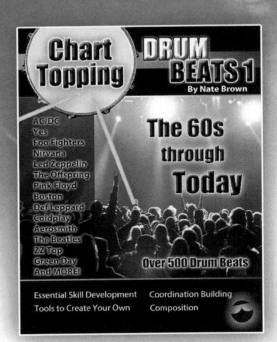

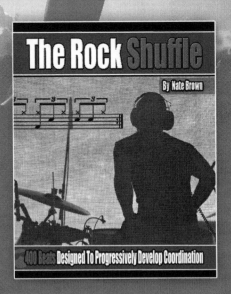

Printed in Great Britain
by Amazon.co.uk, Ltd.,
Marston Gate.